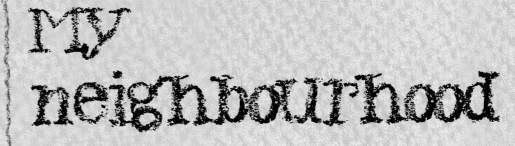

My neighbourhood

It's quiet where Lily lives. There are lots of trees and there's a park where all the kids can play.
The children who live in Lily's street often walk to the park to play.
They're more than just neighbours — they are really good friends.

Come out to play!

What a beautiful day! The sun is out and it's very warm. As soon as the neighbourhood kids wake up, they all want to go and play in the park. There will be lots of other kids playing there so they know they'll all have great fun.

Peter

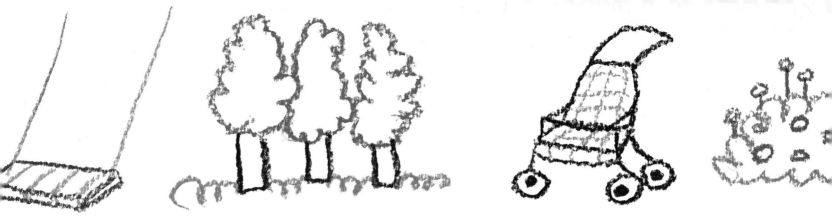

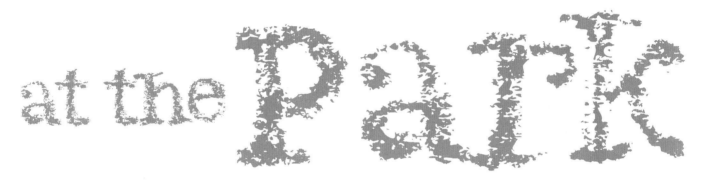

Manners at the Park

Arianna Candell · Rosa M. Curto

BOOK HOUSE

Lily

Carla

Julia

Hold my hand

Paul

Paul has two sisters, Julia and Carla. Their father is taking them to the park so they can play. Paul is in a huff because he has to hold his father's hand. He thinks he's old enough to walk down the street by himself now. But Julia knows that it's safer if she holds her father's hand.

stay in your buggy

Rosie's little sister Rita sits in her buggy, although she can walk for short distances. When she sees that her big sister Rosie is walking, she wants to get out of her buggy and walk too. Rosie tells her that they can go much faster if she stays in her buggy and they will get to the park much quicker that way.

Rosie

Rita

Mo

Peter

Mark

Paul

David

Anna

Jim

We are all here

All the kids are in the park now. Jim, Anna and Mark are blowing bubbles. Peter and Mo are roller-skating. Rachel and Maria are feeding the squirrels, and the rest of the kids are all playing with a ball.

Lucy

Rachel

Maria

Please do not drop litter

A few days ago it was Rachel and Maria's birthday, so today they are sharing some of their sweets with their friends. David has forgotten to throw all the sweetie wrappers in the waste bin. A gust of wind suddenly blows the wrappers all over the ground. John sees what has happened and he gets the other kids together to help pick up all the litter.

Maria

Julia

Rachel

David

Lucy

John

Do you have a dog?

Jim loves dogs and he would really like to have one. When he sees a dog in the park, he always stops to watch it. Today Jim meets Peter, who's taking his dog for a walk. Peter tells him that having a pet is a big responsibility.

Peter

Jim

You have to feed and wash your dog and take it for a walk every day. You also have to clean up any mess it leaves on the street or in the park. Peter reminds Jim not to pat a strange dog until he has asked the owner if it's OK.

Come and see the ducks!

Lily   Anna

There is a small pond in the park and a whole family of ducks lives there. They are so pretty, and Lily and Anna are quietly watching them. They know that ducks like peace and quiet, so they never shout or clap their hands because that would scare them away.

Rosie

Julia

Mo

Wait for your turn!

Rosie loves the swings so much that she could spend the whole day there! She doesn't see the other kids waiting for a turn, so the queue is getting longer and longer. Finally, Mo reminds her that everything in the park has to be shared.

Maria

Adrian

David

Rachel

Peter

Can we play, too?

Lily and Anna are back from the duck pond now, and they would like to join in skipping with the others. Maria tells them that there are already enough kids playing so they should find something else to do. The others say that they can join in and the game will be even more fun.

Rosie

Adrian

Paul

Mark

Julia

Jim

A new bike

Jim and Mark are racing around the park on their bikes.
Mark is going so fast that he almost knocks Julia over. They
both get a fright, but luckily no-one is hurt. Julia still feels
shaky and reminds Mark that the park is full of other people.
She tells him to slow down before he does hurt someone.

Peter, Mark, Rachel and Maria are tired and stop for a rest. They sit on a bench to read a story. Rachel sees her Grandad who is looking for somewhere to sit to read his newspaper. She asks the others to make room for him so he can share their bench.

Come and sit here!

Rachel

Peter

Watch the traffic lights

Lily is learning about road safety at school: always cross the street at a pedestrian crossing, and look left and right to check if any cars are coming. Today she is teaching this to her little brother on their way home. She tells him that he must never step onto a pedestrian crossing if the green man has turned to red, even if there are no cars coming. She also reminds him that it is always safer to hold a grown-up's hand to cross the street.

Lily

George

What a happy neighbourhood

The kids are lucky to live in such a quiet and peaceful neighbourhood with a park so close to home. They are good neighbours because they all know how to live and play together so that everyone can have a great time!

Julia

Rachel

Maria

Mark

Adrian

Anna

Activities

All of the following activities are perfect for the park or a neighbour's garden. These are outdoor activities because the children will need plenty of space to play.

EARTH, WIND, WATER!

This game will test who has the fastest reactions.

You have to have at least three players: the leader gives the instructions for the other players to follow. A line is drawn on the ground, and the players stand on one side of it. When the leader says 'water', the players must jump over to the other side of the line, keeping their feet together; if the leader says 'wind', they must stay on the same side of the line and just jump up in the air; if the leader says 'earth', the players must stay where they are but hop on one foot. The leader can choose to give the instructions in any order and as fast as she wishes. In this way she tries to trick the players, who have to listen carefully so they won't make mistakes. The player who does not react quickly enough or follow the directions is out of the game.

Mark

John

Lucy

THE BURSTING BALLOON

Someone must blow up a balloon. One player is chosen to be the 'clock'. The other players must sit in a circle around 'the clock' who is then blindfolded. When the 'clock' says 'now', the other players start passing the balloon around. As they are passing it back and forth, the 'clock' silently counts up to thirty, as fast as she likes.

As she is counting in her head, the other players can't tell how fast she is going. When the 'clock' gets to twenty-five, she warns them that the balloon is just about to pop. When she reaches thirty, she says, 'POP'. Whoever is holding the balloon is then OUT and has to leave the game. The winner is the last player left, who will then be the 'clock' in the next round of the game.

Peter   Rosie

Paul

David

Lily   Anna

STEP ON THE TAIL

Each player needs a piece of rope to tuck into their waistband, as if it were a tail. The rope should be long enough to hang down with about 30 cm resting on the ground. When the game starts, all the players must try to step on each others tails while trying to keep their own tails safe. When a player loses her tail, she is out of the game. The last player to keep his tail is the winner.

Adrian

Anna

GIANT BUBBLES

As this game is wet and messy, it has to be played outdoors. To make giant bubbles, you will need a cup of water, two tablespoons of glycerin, two tablespoons of washing-up liquid, and a piece of wire that is about 30 cm long. Ask a grown-up to make the wire into a large circular ring with a small handle. Put all the ingredients into a flat, wide container and mix well. Then dip the wire ring into it. Swing the ring in a long, smooth motion to make huge soap bubbles.

FOLLOW THE LEADER

This game is played by following whatever the leader does.

Someone is chosen to be the leader, and the other players stand right behind her. When she starts walking, all the others follow and do whatever the leader does. The leader may choose to jump, crouch down, move forward or backward, hop on one foot... or anything.

She may do whatever she wants, even if it looks silly to the other players!

Each player gets a chance to be the leader.

Paul Rachel Jim Maria

Guidelines for parents

COURTESY AND RESPECTFULNESS

How can we teach small children to be considerate of others? These books may be helpful in providing examples that stress the importance of showing good manners and of living our lives without upsetting people around us. In fact, you can start by simply asking children to think about what they don't like themselves, so that they can avoid doing these things to others and make life better for everyone. We must all live together peacefully and respect one another, not just in our own families but also in our neighbourhoods, our schools and our towns.

Living alongside other people means we also need to consider their feelings and rights. We should follow certain rules of behaviour so everyone will feel comfortable. In order to explain this concept, we can use a variety of daily situations. For example, it's very annoying to get chewing gum stuck to the bottom of your shoe, isn't it? Well, the solution is not to throw chewing gum on the floor or street.

DIVERSITY

We should remind small children that we are not all alike. It is important that they learn to think about the different ways people live in a community. They need to know that a blind person cannot cross the street without help. A person in a wheelchair needs a clear passage. An elderly person may need someone to hold open a door. It is also necessary to explain that when using public transport, it is kind to offer your seat to those who are disabled, elderly or pregnant. Being courteous, helpful, and considerate are values that never go out of fashion and are always appreciated.

    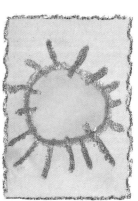 

RESPECT TRAFFIC LIGHTS

It is so important to pay attention to traffic lights and obey them! When talking to your children about road safety, you should have a positive attitude. Emphasise what they should do and also what they shouldn't do. Explaining rules to children is not enough, as they will learn much more readily if we provide examples. If they learn the basic rules from early childhood (only cross at the pedestrian crossing; stop if a red man is showing, etc.), they will learn to respect these rules as they grow older. When they are old enough to drive, they often follow their parents' behaviour on the road. Youngsters pay close attention to their parents' example, so it's most important that we demonstrate our best behaviour to them as pedestrians and drivers.

WAITING FOR YOUR TURN

Parks are public places filled with many children. It's important that youngsters understand that everything in the park must be shared.

The adults must help the children to understand this. Since adults bring small children to the park, it's up to the adults to keep a close eye on them, reminding them about taking turns and other good behaviour. Using a swing in a park is not the same as using a swing that's in your own back garden.

DO YOU HAVE A DOG?

Many children dream of having a pet but don't understand the responsibility of pet ownership. Even those who own pets may not be as responsible as they should be. To the best of their ability, children should be encouraged to take care of their own pet. An adult can determine which tasks will best teach responsibility within the child's capabilities. One task could be walking the dog and picking up after it. Remind the child that a park where small children are playing is not a good place to walk a dog. Dogs are a reflection of their owners, so we must be careful not to allow our pets to disturb others.

Published in Great Britain in MMXII by
Book House, an imprint of
The Salariya Book Company Ltd
25 Marlborough Place, Brighton BN1 1UB
www.salariya.com
www.book-house.co.uk

1 3 5 7 9 8 6 4 2

A CIP catalogue record for this book is available
from the British Library.

Printed and bound in China.

PB ISBN: 978-1-908177-10-0

Original title of the book in Catalan: Com ens hem de comportar al parc
© MMV Gemser Publications S.L.